Introduction

CW00666593

This edition of the *Accident Book* BI 510 has been issued by the Health and Safety Executive (HSE), which is sponsored by the Department for Work and Pensions (DWP). Employers and employees can use this book to record details of work-related injuries for which state benefits could be payable. See pages 2–3 for more information.

The *Accident Book* is a valuable document that organisations can use to record accident information as part of their management of health and safety.
An involved and fully informed workforce is the basis of good health and safety management. See below and page 5.

The *Accident Book* can be used to record details of injuries that employers must report under the Reporting of Injuries, Diseases and Dangerous Occurrences Regulations (RIDDOR). See page 4.

Safety representatives are legally entitled to accident records that employers have to keep, by law. A tick box is included on each accident record form asking whether the injured person gives their consent to the disclosure of the information contained in that record to safety representatives, to enable them to carry out their statutory functions more effectively.

The format of this book has been designed to protect the privacy of personal information and to comply with the EU General Data Protection Regulation (GDPR). Individual accident records can be removed and stored securely. This will help you to keep personal information in confidence.

This edition of the *Accident Book* will help you comply with legal requirements under social security and health and safety legislation, and to share information with safety representatives, taking confidentiality fully into account.

About this book:
To the employer

This book satisfies the social security regulations and RIDDOR about keeping records of accidents to people at work.

Recording accidents at work

To comply with social security regulations, you must keep a record of injuries that happen to employees if you own or occupy:

- a factory, mine or quarry;
- works or premises where the Factories Act 1961 applies;
- any other premises in which (or around which) you employ ten or more people at the same time.

To do this you should provide an accident book such as this one in which employees, or people acting on their behalf, can enter details of accidents leading to injury. It should be kept in a place where any employee can find it at all reasonable times.

You can use this book to keep records of accidents to people at work that are reportable under RIDDOR.

How to use this book

- Employers are required under both statute law and the common law to keep personal information confidential.
- Information can be disclosed if, for example, there is a statutory requirement to do so; or an individual has consented to their personal information being disclosed to a third party, such as a safety representative. You should nominate a member of your staff to be responsible for the safekeeping of completed accident records. Enter their name, and your work address, on the INSIDE FRONT COVER of this book.
- Employers must disclose the personal information and details of the accident to safety representatives and/or representatives of employee safety, if the injured person ticks the tick box and signs. If the injured person does not consent to the disclosure of this personal information, you must anonymise the information before disclosing it to safety representatives and/or representatives of employee safety.
- The arrangements to pass on this information should be discussed between employers, employees and/or their representatives. The aim should be to make the best possible use of this (and other) information to meet health and safety objectives.

- You must also enter a number in the box on the front cover of this book to ensure identification. Number the books in sequence (eg if this is the first book that you have used, enter 1, if it is the second, enter 2 etc).
- Now number each of the accident records in the corresponding report number box (eg enter 1 in the report number box on the first page, 2 in the box on the second page and so on). This number must be filled in twice: once on the actual record, and the other on the stub.
- An injured employee, or someone acting on their behalf, must complete an accident record as soon as they can.
- Completed accident records should be detached from this book, passed to the nominated person, and stored securely (eg in a lockable cabinet) in compliance with GDPR.
- You must investigate the cause of each accident recorded. If you find anything different from the information provided, you should make a note in section 3 of the record to say what you found.
- Do not dispose of the book covers after the last record has been completed and removed for storage. Instead, keep the covers in a safe place, so the accident records can be matched to the stubs.
- You must keep each accident record, and each set of book covers, for at least three years.

The recording, by you, of injuries arising from accidents at work

You can use this book if you want to record people's injuries from accidents at work, which the law requires you to report and record. When you use this book for this reason:

- you will have to complete section 5 of the accident record;
- sign section 5, as well as section 3.

Reporting of Injuries, Diseases and Dangerous Occurrences Regulations (RIDDOR)

As well as keeping records like the ones in this book, RIDDOR states that you must notify, report and record some deaths and injuries that arise from accidents at work.

You must produce RIDDOR records when asked by HSE or local authority inspectors.

You must also make RIDDOR records available to safety representatives either by asking the injured person to consent to the release of the record, or by presenting relevant information about the accident in an anonymised form when consent has not been obtained.

Safety representatives must have access to this important safety information as required under legislation. HSE is committed to encouraging and developing partnerships between employers and safety representatives to ensure that co-operation, including sharing appropriate information, is the usual practice, not the exception, in the workplace.

You also have to report some work-related diseases, but reporting arrangements are different. For the full list of reportable diseases, visit the HSE website www.hse.gov.uk/riddor.

This is only a summary of the law on RIDDOR. HSE's website contains up-to-date information about what you must do and what records you need to keep. Go to www.hse.gov.uk/riddor/index.htm.

How do I notify and report?

Online
Go to www.hse.gov.uk/riddor/report.htm and complete the appropriate online report form. The form will then be submitted directly to the RIDDOR database. You will receive a copy for your records.

Telephone
All incidents can be reported online but a telephone service is also provided for reporting fatal/specified and major incidents only – call the Incident Contact Centre on 0345 300 9923 (opening hours Monday to Friday 8.30 am to 5 pm).

First aid

You must provide adequate and appropriate equipment, facilities and people, so first aid can be given to employees if they are injured or become ill at work.

HSE's advice on all aspects of first aid at work can be found on the HSE website at www.hse.gov.uk/firstaid/index.htm.

About this book:
To the employee

When you are injured at work, the law says you have to tell your employer as soon as you can. You can do this by recording your accident in this book. Anyone else can do this on your behalf. Recording your accident will help you to protect your right to state benefits.

How to use this book

- Complete the accident record, giving your personal details and details about your accident. Answer each question that applies to you. Do not complete section 5 of the record sheet, called 'For the employer only'.
- Complete or leave blank the tick box in section 4 of the accident record. The tick box is to allow you to indicate whether you are happy for the personal information about you and your accident to be given to safety representatives and representatives of employee safety, solely for the purpose of enabling them to carry out the health and safety functions given to them by law.
- When you have filled in the accident record, tear it out and hand it to the person named on the front of this book as responsible for securely storing accident records in compliance with GDPR. Your employer can pass this information on if they have a statutory duty to do so to, for example, a safety representative. Your personal information will be anonymised if you have not ticked the box in section 4.
- You may wish to make a photocopy of the accident record before handing it in. You should also keep a note of the report number of the accident record and of the number on the front cover of the *Accident Book*.

Advice about benefits

- **If the accident stops you from working**
  Your employer may pay your sick pay from a private sick pay scheme. Whether or not this is paid, you should be entitled to Statutory Sick Pay (SSP). If you do not qualify for sick pay or SSP from your employer, you may be able to get other state benefits. Look on the GOV.UK website at: www.gov.uk.
- **If the accident disables you**
  You may be entitled to Industrial Injuries Disablement Benefit. You can find more information on the GOV.UK website at: www.gov.uk/industrial-injuries-disablement-benefit or phone the benefit enquiry helpline on 0800 121 8379.

Accident record

1 About the person who had the accident

Name _____

Address _____

_____ Postcode _____

Occupation _____

2 About you, the person filling in this record

i *If you did not have the accident write your address and occupation.*

Name _____

Address _____

_____ Postcode _____

Occupation _____

3 About the accident

i *Continue on the back of this form if you need to.*

When it happened. Date _____ Time _____

Where it happened. State room or place _____

_____

How the accident happened. Give the cause if you can _____

_____

_____

_____

If the person who had the accident suffered an injury, say what it was _____

_____

Please sign the record and date it. Signature _____ Date _____

4 For the employee only

☐ By ticking this box I give my consent to my employer to disclose my personal information and details of the accident which appear on this form to safety representatives and representatives of employee safety for them to carry out the health and safety functions given to them by law.

Signature _____ Date _____

5 For the employer only

Complete this box if the accident is reportable under the Reporting of Injuries, Diseases and Dangerous Occurrences Regulations (RIDDOR). To report, go to page 4 of this book or go to **http://www.hse.gov.uk/riddor/report.htm**

Please sign the record and date it. Signature _____ Date _____

Accident record

1 About the person who had the accident

Name

Address

Postcode

Occupation

2 About you, the person filling in this record

i *If you did not have the accident write your address and occupation.*

Name

Address

Postcode

Occupation

3 About the accident

i *Continue on the back of this form if you need to.*

When it happened. Date _____ Time _____

Where it happened. State room or place _____

How the accident happened. Give the cause if you can _____

If the person who had the accident suffered an injury, say what it was _____

Please sign the record and date it. Signature _____ Date _____

4 For the employee only

☐ By ticking this box I give my consent to my employer to disclose my personal information and details of the accident which appear on this form to safety representatives and representatives of employee safety for them to carry out the health and safety functions given to them by law.

Signature _____ Date _____

5 For the employer only

Complete this box if the accident is reportable under the Reporting of Injuries, Diseases and Dangerous Occurrences Regulations (RIDDOR). To report, go to page 4 of this book or go to
http://www.hse.gov.uk/riddor/report.htm

Please sign the record and date it. Signature _____ Date _____

Accident record

1 About the person who had the accident

Name _____

Address _____

Postcode _____

Occupation _____

2 About you, the person filling in this record

i *If you did not have the accident write your address and occupation.*

Name _____

Address _____

Postcode _____

Occupation _____

3 About the accident

i *Continue on the back of this form if you need to.*

When it happened. Date _____ Time _____

Where it happened. State room or place _____

_____

How the accident happened. Give the cause if you can _____

_____

_____

_____

If the person who had the accident suffered an injury, say what it was _____

_____

Please sign the record and date it. Signature _____ Date _____

4 For the employee only

☐ By ticking this box I give my consent to my employer to disclose my personal information and details of the accident which appear on this form to safety representatives and representatives of employee safety for them to carry out the health and safety functions given to them by law.

Signature _____ Date _____

5 For the employer only

Complete this box if the accident is reportable under the Reporting of Injuries, Diseases and Dangerous Occurrences Regulations (RIDDOR). To report, go to page 4 of this book or go to **http://www.hse.gov.uk/riddor/report.htm**

Please sign the record and date it. Signature _____ Date _____

Accident record

1 About the person who had the accident

Name _____

Address _____

Postcode

_____

Occupation _____

2 About you, the person filling in this record

i *If you did not have the accident write your address and occupation.*

Name _____

Address _____

Postcode

_____

Occupation _____

3 About the accident

i *Continue on the back of this form if you need to.*

When it happened. Date _____ Time _____

Where it happened. State room or place _____

_____

How the accident happened. Give the cause if you can _____

_____

_____

_____

If the person who had the accident suffered an injury, say what it was _____

_____

Please sign the record and date it. Signature _____ Date _____

4 For the employee only

☐ By ticking this box I give my consent to my employer to disclose my personal information and details of the accident which appear on this form to safety representatives and representatives of employee safety for them to carry out the health and safety functions given to them by law.

Signature _____ Date _____

5 For the employer only

Complete this box if the accident is reportable under the Reporting of Injuries, Diseases and Dangerous Occurrences Regulations (RIDDOR). To report, go to page 4 of this book or go to **http://www.hse.gov.uk/riddor/report.htm**

Please sign the record and date it. Signature _____ Date _____

Accident record

1   About the person who had the accident

Name

Address

Postcode

Occupation

2   About you, the person filling in this record

i   *If you did not have the accident write your address and occupation.*

Name

Address

Postcode

Occupation

3   About the accident

i   *Continue on the back of this form if you need to.*

When it happened. Date _____ Time _____

Where it happened. State room or place _____

_____

How the accident happened. Give the cause if you can _____

_____

_____

_____

If the person who had the accident suffered an injury, say what it was _____

_____

Please sign the record and date it. Signature _____ Date _____

4   For the employee only

☐   By ticking this box I give my consent to my employer to disclose my personal information and details of the accident which appear on this form to safety representatives and representatives of employee safety for them to carry out the health and safety functions given to them by law.

Signature _____ Date _____

5   For the employer only

Complete this box if the accident is reportable under the Reporting of Injuries, Diseases and Dangerous Occurrences Regulations (RIDDOR). To report, go to page 4 of this book or go to
http://www.hse.gov.uk/riddor/report.htm

Please sign the record and date it. Signature _____ Date _____

Accident record

1   About the person who had the accident

Name _____

Address _____

_____ Postcode _____

Occupation _____

2   About you, the person filling in this record

i   *If you did not have the accident write your address and occupation.*

Name _____

Address _____

_____ Postcode _____

Occupation _____

3   About the accident

i   *Continue on the back of this form if you need to.*

When it happened. Date _____ Time _____

Where it happened. State room or place _____

_____

How the accident happened. Give the cause if you can _____

_____

_____

_____

If the person who had the accident suffered an injury, say what it was _____

_____

Please sign the record and date it. Signature _____ Date _____

4   For the employee only

[ ]   By ticking this box I give my consent to my employer to disclose my personal information and details of the accident which appear on this form to safety representatives and representatives of employee safety for them to carry out the health and safety functions given to them by law.

Signature _____ Date _____

5   For the employer only

Complete this box if the accident is reportable under the Reporting of Injuries, Diseases and Dangerous Occurrences Regulations (RIDDOR). To report, go to page 4 of this book or go to **http://www.hse.gov.uk/riddor/report.htm**

Please sign the record and date it. Signature _____ Date _____

Accident record

1 About the person who had the accident

Name _____

Address _____

_____ Postcode _____

Occupation _____

2 About you, the person filling in this record

i *If you did not have the accident write your address and occupation.*

Name _____

Address _____

_____ Postcode _____

Occupation _____

3 About the accident

i *Continue on the back of this form if you need to.*

When it happened. Date _____ Time _____

Where it happened. State room or place _____

_____

How the accident happened. Give the cause if you can _____

_____

_____

_____

If the person who had the accident suffered an injury, say what it was _____

_____

Please sign the record and date it. Signature _____ Date _____

4 For the employee only

☐ By ticking this box I give my consent to my employer to disclose my personal information and details of the accident which appear on this form to safety representatives and representatives of employee safety for them to carry out the health and safety functions given to them by law.

Signature _____ Date _____

5 For the employer only

Complete this box if the accident is reportable under the Reporting of Injuries, Diseases and Dangerous Occurrences Regulations (RIDDOR). To report, go to page 4 of this book or go to **http://www.hse.gov.uk/riddor/report.htm**

Please sign the record and date it. Signature _____ Date _____

Report number:

Report number:

Accident record

1 About the person who had the accident

Name

Address

Postcode

Occupation

2 About you, the person filling in this record

i *If you did not have the accident write your address and occupation.*

Name

Address

Postcode

Occupation

3 About the accident

i *Continue on the back of this form if you need to.*

When it happened. Date _____ Time _____

Where it happened. State room or place _____

How the accident happened. Give the cause if you can _____

If the person who had the accident suffered an injury, say what it was _____

Please sign the record and date it. Signature _____ Date _____

4 For the employee only

☐ By ticking this box I give my consent to my employer to disclose my personal information and details of the accident which appear on this form to safety representatives and representatives of employee safety for them to carry out the health and safety functions given to them by law.

Signature _____ Date _____

5 For the employer only

Complete this box if the accident is reportable under the Reporting of Injuries, Diseases and Dangerous Occurrences Regulations (RIDDOR). To report, go to page 4 of this book or go to
http://www.hse.gov.uk/riddor/report.htm

Please sign the record and date it. Signature _____ Date _____

Accident record

1   About the person who had the accident

Name

Address

Postcode

Occupation

2   About you, the person filling in this record

i   *If you did not have the accident write your address and occupation.*

Name

Address

Postcode

Occupation

3   About the accident

i   *Continue on the back of this form if you need to.*

When it happened. Date _____ Time _____

Where it happened. State room or place _____

_____

How the accident happened. Give the cause if you can _____

_____

_____

_____

If the person who had the accident suffered an injury, say what it was _____

_____

Please sign the record and date it. Signature _____ Date _____

4   For the employee only

[ ]   By ticking this box I give my consent to my employer to disclose my personal information and details of the accident which appear on this form to safety representatives and representatives of employee safety for them to carry out the health and safety functions given to them by law.

Signature _____ Date _____

5   For the employer only

Complete this box if the accident is reportable under the Reporting of Injuries, Diseases and Dangerous Occurrences Regulations (RIDDOR). To report, go to page 4 of this book or go to **http://www.hse.gov.uk/riddor/report.htm**

Please sign the record and date it. Signature _____ Date _____

Accident record

1   About the person who had the accident

Name

Address

Postcode

Occupation

2   About you, the person filling in this record

i *If you did not have the accident write your address and occupation.*

Name

Address

Postcode

Occupation

3   About the accident

i *Continue on the back of this form if you need to.*

When it happened. Date _____ Time _____

Where it happened. State room or place _____

How the accident happened. Give the cause if you can _____

If the person who had the accident suffered an injury, say what it was _____

Please sign the record and date it. Signature _____ Date _____

4   For the employee only

☐ By ticking this box I give my consent to my employer to disclose my personal information and details of the accident which appear on this form to safety representatives and representatives of employee safety for them to carry out the health and safety functions given to them by law.

Signature _____ Date _____

5   For the employer only

Complete this box if the accident is reportable under the Reporting of Injuries, Diseases and Dangerous Occurrences Regulations (RIDDOR). To report, go to page 4 of this book or go to **http://www.hse.gov.uk/riddor/report.htm**

Please sign the record and date it. Signature _____ Date _____

Accident record

1   About the person who had the accident

Name

Address

Postcode

Occupation

2   About you, the person filling in this record

i *If you did not have the accident write your address and occupation.*

Name

Address

Postcode

Occupation

3   About the accident

i *Continue on the back of this form if you need to.*

When it happened. Date _____ Time _____

Where it happened. State room or place _____

How the accident happened. Give the cause if you can _____

If the person who had the accident suffered an injury, say what it was _____

Please sign the record and date it. Signature _____ Date _____

4   For the employee only

[ ] By ticking this box I give my consent to my employer to disclose my personal information and details of the accident which appear on this form to safety representatives and representatives of employee safety for them to carry out the health and safety functions given to them by law.

Signature _____ Date _____

5   For the employer only

Complete this box if the accident is reportable under the Reporting of Injuries, Diseases and Dangerous Occurrences Regulations (RIDDOR). To report, go to page 4 of this book or go to **http://www.hse.gov.uk/riddor/report.htm**

Please sign the record and date it. Signature _____ Date _____

Accident record

Report number:

Report number:

1 About the person who had the accident

Name

Address

Postcode

Occupation

2 About you, the person filling in this record

i *If you did not have the accident write your address and occupation.*

Name

Address

Postcode

Occupation

3 About the accident

i *Continue on the back of this form if you need to.*

When it happened. Date _____ Time _____

Where it happened. State room or place _____

_____

How the accident happened. Give the cause if you can _____

_____

_____

_____

If the person who had the accident suffered an injury, say what it was _____

_____

Please sign the record and date it. Signature _____ Date _____

4 For the employee only

☐ By ticking this box I give my consent to my employer to disclose my personal information and details of the accident which appear on this form to safety representatives and representatives of employee safety for them to carry out the health and safety functions given to them by law.

Signature _____ Date _____

5 For the employer only

Complete this box if the accident is reportable under the Reporting of Injuries, Diseases and Dangerous Occurrences Regulations (RIDDOR). To report, go to page 4 of this book or go to **http://www.hse.gov.uk/riddor/report.htm**

Please sign the record and date it. Signature _____ Date _____

Accident record

1 About the person who had the accident

Name _____

Address _____

Postcode _____

Occupation _____

2 About you, the person filling in this record

ⓘ *If you did not have the accident write your address and occupation.*

Name _____

Address _____

Postcode _____

Occupation _____

3 About the accident

ⓘ *Continue on the back of this form if you need to.*

When it happened. Date _____ Time _____

Where it happened. State room or place _____
_____

How the accident happened. Give the cause if you can _____
_____
_____
_____

If the person who had the accident suffered an injury, say what it was _____
_____

Please sign the record and date it. Signature _____ Date _____

4 For the employee only

☐ By ticking this box I give my consent to my employer to disclose my personal information and details of the accident which appear on this form to safety representatives and representatives of employee safety for them to carry out the health and safety functions given to them by law.

Signature _____ Date _____

5 For the employer only

Complete this box if the accident is reportable under the Reporting of Injuries, Diseases and Dangerous Occurrences Regulations (RIDDOR). To report, go to page 4 of this book or go to **http://www.hse.gov.uk/riddor/report.htm**

Please sign the record and date it. Signature _____ Date _____

Accident record

1 About the person who had the accident

Name

Address

Postcode

Occupation

2 About you, the person filling in this record

i *If you did not have the accident write your address and occupation.*

Name

Address

Postcode

Occupation

3 About the accident

i *Continue on the back of this form if you need to.*

When it happened. Date _____ Time _____

Where it happened. State room or place _____

How the accident happened. Give the cause if you can _____

If the person who had the accident suffered an injury, say what it was _____

Please sign the record and date it. Signature _____ Date _____

4 For the employee only

☐ By ticking this box I give my consent to my employer to disclose my personal information and details of the accident which appear on this form to safety representatives and representatives of employee safety for them to carry out the health and safety functions given to them by law.

Signature _____ Date _____

5 For the employer only

Complete this box if the accident is reportable under the Reporting of Injuries, Diseases and Dangerous Occurrences Regulations (RIDDOR). To report, go to page 4 of this book or go to
http://www.hse.gov.uk/riddor/report.htm

Please sign the record and date it. Signature _____ Date _____

Accident record

1 About the person who had the accident

Name _____

Address _____

_____ Postcode _____

Occupation _____

2 About you, the person filling in this record

i *If you did not have the accident write your address and occupation.*

Name _____

Address _____

_____ Postcode _____

Occupation _____

3 About the accident

i *Continue on the back of this form if you need to.*

When it happened. Date _____ Time _____

Where it happened. State room or place _____

_____

How the accident happened. Give the cause if you can _____

_____

_____

_____

If the person who had the accident suffered an injury, say what it was _____

_____

Please sign the record and date it. Signature _____ Date _____

4 For the employee only

☐ By ticking this box I give my consent to my employer to disclose my personal information and details of the accident which appear on this form to safety representatives and representatives of employee safety for them to carry out the health and safety functions given to them by law.

Signature _____ Date _____

5 For the employer only

Complete this box if the accident is reportable under the Reporting of Injuries, Diseases and Dangerous Occurrences Regulations (RIDDOR). To report, go to page 4 of this book or go to **http://www.hse.gov.uk/riddor/report.htm**

Please sign the record and date it. Signature _____ Date _____

Accident record

1 About the person who had the accident

Name _____

Address _____

Postcode

_____

Occupation _____

2 About you, the person filling in this record

i *If you did not have the accident write your address and occupation.*

Name _____

Address _____

Postcode

_____

Occupation _____

3 About the accident

i *Continue on the back of this form if you need to.*

When it happened. Date _____ Time _____

Where it happened. State room or place _____

_____

How the accident happened. Give the cause if you can _____

_____

_____

_____

If the person who had the accident suffered an injury, say what it was _____

_____

Please sign the record and date it. Signature _____ Date _____

4 For the employee only

☐ By ticking this box I give my consent to my employer to disclose my personal information and details of the accident which appear on this form to safety representatives and representatives of employee safety for them to carry out the health and safety functions given to them by law.

Signature _____ Date _____

5 For the employer only

Complete this box if the accident is reportable under the Reporting of Injuries, Diseases and Dangerous Occurrences Regulations (RIDDOR). To report, go to page 4 of this book or go to **http://www.hse.gov.uk/riddor/report.htm**

Please sign the record and date it. Signature _____ Date _____

Accident record

1 About the person who had the accident

Name

Address

Postcode

Occupation

2 About you, the person filling in this record

i *If you did not have the accident write your address and occupation.*

Name

Address

Postcode

Occupation

3 About the accident

i *Continue on the back of this form if you need to.*

When it happened. Date _____ Time _____

Where it happened. State room or place _____

How the accident happened. Give the cause if you can _____

If the person who had the accident suffered an injury, say what it was _____

Please sign the record and date it. Signature _____ Date _____

4 For the employee only

☐ By ticking this box I give my consent to my employer to disclose my personal information and details of the accident which appear on this form to safety representatives and representatives of employee safety for them to carry out the health and safety functions given to them by law.

Signature _____ Date _____

5 For the employer only

Complete this box if the accident is reportable under the Reporting of Injuries, Diseases and Dangerous Occurrences Regulations (RIDDOR). To report, go to page 4 of this book or go to **http://www.hse.gov.uk/riddor/report.htm**

Please sign the record and date it. Signature _____ Date _____

Accident record

1   About the person who had the accident

Name

Address

Postcode

Occupation

2   About you, the person filling in this record

i   *If you did not have the accident write your address and occupation.*

Name

Address

Postcode

Occupation

3   About the accident

i   *Continue on the back of this form if you need to.*

When it happened. Date _____ Time _____

Where it happened. State room or place _____

How the accident happened. Give the cause if you can _____

If the person who had the accident suffered an injury, say what it was _____

Please sign the record and date it. Signature _____ Date _____

4   For the employee only

☐ By ticking this box I give my consent to my employer to disclose my personal information and details of the accident which appear on this form to safety representatives and representatives of employee safety for them to carry out the health and safety functions given to them by law.

Signature _____ Date _____

5   For the employer only

Complete this box if the accident is reportable under the Reporting of Injuries, Diseases and Dangerous Occurrences Regulations (RIDDOR). To report, go to page 4 of this book or go to **http://www.hse.gov.uk/riddor/report.htm**

Please sign the record and date it. Signature _____ Date _____

Report number:

Report number:

Accident record

1   About the person who had the accident

Name _____

Address _____

                                             Postcode _____

_____

Occupation _____

2   About you, the person filling in this record

ℹ️ *If you did not have the accident write your address and occupation.*

Name _____

Address _____

                                             Postcode _____

_____

Occupation _____

3   About the accident

ℹ️ *Continue on the back of this form if you need to.*

When it happened. Date _____ Time _____

Where it happened. State room or place _____

_____

How the accident happened. Give the cause if you can _____

_____

_____

_____

If the person who had the accident suffered an injury, say what it was _____

_____

Please sign the record and date it. Signature _____ Date _____

---

4   For the employee only

☐ By ticking this box I give my consent to my employer to disclose my personal information and details of the accident which appear on this form to safety representatives and representatives of employee safety for them to carry out the health and safety functions given to them by law.

Signature _____ Date _____

---

5   For the employer only

Complete this box if the accident is reportable under the Reporting of Injuries, Diseases and Dangerous Occurrences Regulations (RIDDOR). To report, go to page 4 of this book or go to **http://www.hse.gov.uk/riddor/report.htm**

Please sign the record and date it. Signature _____ Date _____

Accident record

1   About the person who had the accident

Name _____

Address _____

Postcode _____

_____

Occupation _____

2   About you, the person filling in this record

i *If you did not have the accident write your address and occupation.*

Name _____

Address _____

Postcode _____

_____

Occupation _____

3   About the accident

i *Continue on the back of this form if you need to.*

When it happened. Date _____ Time _____

Where it happened. State room or place _____

_____

How the accident happened. Give the cause if you can _____

_____

_____

_____

If the person who had the accident suffered an injury, say what it was _____

_____

Please sign the record and date it. Signature _____ Date _____

4   For the employee only

☐ By ticking this box I give my consent to my employer to disclose my personal information and details of the accident which appear on this form to safety representatives and representatives of employee safety for them to carry out the health and safety functions given to them by law.

Signature _____ Date _____

5   For the employer only

Complete this box if the accident is reportable under the Reporting of Injuries, Diseases and Dangerous Occurrences Regulations (RIDDOR). To report, go to page 4 of this book or go to **http://www.hse.gov.uk/riddor/report.htm**

Please sign the record and date it. Signature _____ Date _____

Accident record

1 About the person who had the accident

Name _____

Address _____

_____ Postcode _____

Occupation _____

2 About you, the person filling in this record

i *If you did not have the accident write your address and occupation.*

Name _____

Address _____

_____ Postcode _____

Occupation _____

3 About the accident

i *Continue on the back of this form if you need to.*

When it happened. Date _____ Time _____

Where it happened. State room or place _____

_____

How the accident happened. Give the cause if you can _____

_____

_____

_____

If the person who had the accident suffered an injury, say what it was _____

_____

Please sign the record and date it. Signature _____ Date _____

4 For the employee only

☐ By ticking this box I give my consent to my employer to disclose my personal information and details of the accident which appear on this form to safety representatives and representatives of employee safety for them to carry out the health and safety functions given to them by law.

Signature _____ Date _____

5 For the employer only

Complete this box if the accident is reportable under the Reporting of Injuries, Diseases and Dangerous Occurrences Regulations (RIDDOR). To report, go to page 4 of this book or go to **http://www.hse.gov.uk/riddor/report.htm**

Please sign the record and date it. Signature _____ Date _____

Accident record

1 About the person who had the accident

Name

Address

Postcode

Occupation

2 About you, the person filling in this record

i *If you did not have the accident write your address and occupation.*

Name

Address

Postcode

Occupation

3 About the accident

i *Continue on the back of this form if you need to.*

When it happened. Date _____ Time _____

Where it happened. State room or place _____

How the accident happened. Give the cause if you can _____

If the person who had the accident suffered an injury, say what it was _____

Please sign the record and date it. Signature _____ Date _____

4 For the employee only

☐ By ticking this box I give my consent to my employer to disclose my personal information and details of the accident which appear on this form to safety representatives and representatives of employee safety for them to carry out the health and safety functions given to them by law.

Signature _____ Date _____

5 For the employer only

Complete this box if the accident is reportable under the Reporting of Injuries, Diseases and Dangerous Occurrences Regulations (RIDDOR). To report, go to page 4 of this book or go to
http://www.hse.gov.uk/riddor/report.htm

Please sign the record and date it. Signature _____ Date _____

Accident record

1 About the person who had the accident

Name

Address

Postcode

Occupation

2 About you, the person filling in this record

i *If you did not have the accident write your address and occupation.*

Name

Address

Postcode

Occupation

3 About the accident

i *Continue on the back of this form if you need to.*

When it happened. Date _____ Time _____

Where it happened. State room or place _____

How the accident happened. Give the cause if you can _____

If the person who had the accident suffered an injury, say what it was _____

Please sign the record and date it. Signature _____ Date _____

4 For the employee only

☐ By ticking this box I give my consent to my employer to disclose my personal information and details of the accident which appear on this form to safety representatives and representatives of employee safety for them to carry out the health and safety functions given to them by law.

Signature _____ Date _____

5 For the employer only

Complete this box if the accident is reportable under the Reporting of Injuries, Diseases and Dangerous Occurrences Regulations (RIDDOR). To report, go to page 4 of this book or go to
http://www.hse.gov.uk/riddor/report.htm

Please sign the record and date it. Signature _____ Date _____

Accident record

1 About the person who had the accident

Name

Address

Postcode

Occupation

2 About you, the person filling in this record

i *If you did not have the accident write your address and occupation.*

Name

Address

Postcode

Occupation

3 About the accident

i *Continue on the back of this form if you need to.*

When it happened. Date _____ Time _____

Where it happened. State room or place _____

_____

How the accident happened. Give the cause if you can _____

_____

_____

_____

If the person who had the accident suffered an injury, say what it was _____

_____

Please sign the record and date it. Signature _____ Date _____

---

4 For the employee only

☐ By ticking this box I give my consent to my employer to disclose my personal information and details of the accident which appear on this form to safety representatives and representatives of employee safety for them to carry out the health and safety functions given to them by law.

Signature _____ Date _____

---

5 For the employer only

Complete this box if the accident is reportable under the Reporting of Injuries, Diseases and Dangerous Occurrences Regulations (RIDDOR). To report, go to page 4 of this book or go to **http://www.hse.gov.uk/riddor/report.htm**

Please sign the record and date it. Signature _____ Date _____

Report number:

Report number:

Accident record

1 About the person who had the accident

Name

Address

Postcode

Occupation

2 About you, the person filling in this record

i *If you did not have the accident write your address and occupation.*

Name

Address

Postcode

Occupation

3 About the accident

i *Continue on the back of this form if you need to.*

When it happened. Date _____ Time _____

Where it happened. State room or place _____

How the accident happened. Give the cause if you can _____

If the person who had the accident suffered an injury, say what it was _____

Please sign the record and date it. Signature _____ Date _____

4 For the employee only

☐ By ticking this box I give my consent to my employer to disclose my personal information and details of the accident which appear on this form to safety representatives and representatives of employee safety for them to carry out the health and safety functions given to them by law.

Signature _____ Date _____

5 For the employer only

Complete this box if the accident is reportable under the Reporting of Injuries, Diseases and Dangerous Occurrences Regulations (RIDDOR). To report, go to page 4 of this book or go to **http://www.hse.gov.uk/riddor/report.htm**

Please sign the record and date it. Signature _____ Date _____

Report number:

Report number:

Accident record

1 About the person who had the accident

Name _____

Address _____

_____ Postcode _____

Occupation _____

2 About you, the person filling in this record

i *If you did not have the accident write your address and occupation.*

Name _____

Address _____

_____ Postcode _____

Occupation _____

3 About the accident

i *Continue on the back of this form if you need to.*

When it happened. Date _____ Time _____

Where it happened. State room or place _____

_____

How the accident happened. Give the cause if you can _____

_____

_____

_____

If the person who had the accident suffered an injury, say what it was _____

_____

Please sign the record and date it. Signature _____ Date _____

4 For the employee only

☐ By ticking this box I give my consent to my employer to disclose my personal information and details of the accident which appear on this form to safety representatives and representatives of employee safety for them to carry out the health and safety functions given to them by law.

Signature _____ Date _____

5 For the employer only

Complete this box if the accident is reportable under the Reporting of Injuries, Diseases and Dangerous Occurrences Regulations (RIDDOR). To report, go to page 4 of this book or go to **http://www.hse.gov.uk/riddor/report.htm**

Please sign the record and date it. Signature _____ Date _____

Accident record

1   About the person who had the accident

Name

Address

Postcode

Occupation

2   About you, the person filling in this record

i *If you did not have the accident write your address and occupation.*

Name

Address

Postcode

Occupation

3   About the accident

i *Continue on the back of this form if you need to.*

When it happened. Date _____ Time _____

Where it happened. State room or place _____

How the accident happened. Give the cause if you can _____

If the person who had the accident suffered an injury, say what it was _____

Please sign the record and date it. Signature _____ Date _____

4   For the employee only

☐ By ticking this box I give my consent to my employer to disclose my personal information and details of the accident which appear on this form to safety representatives and representatives of employee safety for them to carry out the health and safety functions given to them by law.

Signature _____ Date _____

5   For the employer only

Complete this box if the accident is reportable under the Reporting of Injuries, Diseases and Dangerous Occurrences Regulations (RIDDOR). To report, go to page 4 of this book or go to **http://www.hse.gov.uk/riddor/report.htm**

Please sign the record and date it. Signature _____ Date _____

Accident record

Report number:

Report number:

1 About the person who had the accident

Name

Address

Postcode

Occupation

2 About you, the person filling in this record

i *If you did not have the accident write your address and occupation.*

Name

Address

Postcode

Occupation

3 About the accident

i *Continue on the back of this form if you need to.*

When it happened. Date _____ Time _____

Where it happened. State room or place _____

How the accident happened. Give the cause if you can _____

If the person who had the accident suffered an injury, say what it was _____

Please sign the record and date it. Signature _____ Date _____

4 For the employee only

☐ By ticking this box I give my consent to my employer to disclose my personal information and details of the accident which appear on this form to safety representatives and representatives of employee safety for them to carry out the health and safety functions given to them by law.

Signature _____ Date _____

5 For the employer only

Complete this box if the accident is reportable under the Reporting of Injuries, Diseases and Dangerous Occurrences Regulations (RIDDOR). To report, go to page 4 of this book or go to **http://www.hse.gov.uk/riddor/report.htm**

Please sign the record and date it. Signature _____ Date _____

Accident record

Report number:

Report number:

1 About the person who had the accident

Name _____

Address _____

_____ Postcode _____

Occupation _____

2 About you, the person filling in this record

i *If you did not have the accident write your address and occupation.*

Name _____

Address _____

_____ Postcode _____

Occupation _____

3 About the accident

i *Continue on the back of this form if you need to.*

When it happened. Date _____ Time _____

Where it happened. State room or place _____

_____

How the accident happened. Give the cause if you can _____

_____

_____

_____

If the person who had the accident suffered an injury, say what it was _____

_____

Please sign the record and date it. Signature _____ Date _____

4 For the employee only

☐ By ticking this box I give my consent to my employer to disclose my personal information and details of the accident which appear on this form to safety representatives and representatives of employee safety for them to carry out the health and safety functions given to them by law.

Signature _____ Date _____

5 For the employer only

Complete this box if the accident is reportable under the Reporting of Injuries, Diseases and Dangerous Occurrences Regulations (RIDDOR). To report, go to page 4 of this book or go to **http://www.hse.gov.uk/riddor/report.htm**

Please sign the record and date it. Signature _____ Date _____

Accident record

1 About the person who had the accident

Name _____

Address _____

Postcode _____

_____

Occupation _____

2 About you, the person filling in this record

i *If you did not have the accident write your address and occupation.*

Name _____

Address _____

Postcode _____

_____

Occupation _____

3 About the accident

i *Continue on the back of this form if you need to.*

When it happened. Date _____ Time _____

Where it happened. State room or place _____

_____

How the accident happened. Give the cause if you can _____

_____

_____

_____

If the person who had the accident suffered an injury, say what it was _____

_____

Please sign the record and date it. Signature _____ Date _____

4 For the employee only

☐ By ticking this box I give my consent to my employer to disclose my personal information and details of the accident which appear on this form to safety representatives and representatives of employee safety for them to carry out the health and safety functions given to them by law.

Signature _____ Date _____

5 For the employer only

Complete this box if the accident is reportable under the Reporting of Injuries, Diseases and Dangerous Occurrences Regulations (RIDDOR). To report, go to page 4 of this book or go to
http://www.hse.gov.uk/riddor/report.htm

Please sign the record and date it. Signature _____ Date _____

Report number:

Report number:

Accident record

1 About the person who had the accident

Name

Address

Postcode

Occupation

2 About you, the person filling in this record

i *If you did not have the accident write your address and occupation.*

Name

Address

Postcode

Occupation

3 About the accident

i *Continue on the back of this form if you need to.*

When it happened. Date _____ Time _____

Where it happened. State room or place _____

How the accident happened. Give the cause if you can _____

If the person who had the accident suffered an injury, say what it was _____

Please sign the record and date it. Signature _____ Date _____

4 For the employee only

☐ By ticking this box I give my consent to my employer to disclose my personal information and details of the accident which appear on this form to safety representatives and representatives of employee safety for them to carry out the health and safety functions given to them by law.

Signature _____ Date _____

5 For the employer only

Complete this box if the accident is reportable under the Reporting of Injuries, Diseases and Dangerous Occurrences Regulations (RIDDOR). To report, go to page 4 of this book or go to **http://www.hse.gov.uk/riddor/report.htm**

Please sign the record and date it. Signature _____ Date _____

Accident record

1 About the person who had the accident

Name _____

Address _____

_____ Postcode _____

Occupation _____

2 About you, the person filling in this record

i *If you did not have the accident write your address and occupation.*

Name _____

Address _____

_____ Postcode _____

Occupation _____

3 About the accident

i *Continue on the back of this form if you need to.*

When it happened. Date _____ Time _____

Where it happened. State room or place _____

_____

How the accident happened. Give the cause if you can _____

_____

_____

_____

If the person who had the accident suffered an injury, say what it was _____

_____

Please sign the record and date it. Signature _____ Date _____

4 For the employee only

☐ By ticking this box I give my consent to my employer to disclose my personal information and details of the accident which appear on this form to safety representatives and representatives of employee safety for them to carry out the health and safety functions given to them by law.

Signature _____ Date _____

5 For the employer only

Complete this box if the accident is reportable under the Reporting of Injuries, Diseases and Dangerous Occurrences Regulations (RIDDOR). To report, go to page 4 of this book or go to **http://www.hse.gov.uk/riddor/report.htm**

Please sign the record and date it. Signature _____ Date _____

Accident record

Report number:

Report number:

1   About the person who had the accident

Name

Address

Postcode

Occupation

2   About you, the person filling in this record

i *If you did not have the accident write your address and occupation.*

Name

Address

Postcode

Occupation

3   About the accident

i *Continue on the back of this form if you need to.*

When it happened. Date _____ Time _____

Where it happened. State room or place _____

How the accident happened. Give the cause if you can _____

If the person who had the accident suffered an injury, say what it was _____

Please sign the record and date it. Signature _____ Date _____

4   For the employee only

☐ By ticking this box I give my consent to my employer to disclose my personal information and details of the accident which appear on this form to safety representatives and representatives of employee safety for them to carry out the health and safety functions given to them by law.

Signature _____ Date _____

5   For the employer only

Complete this box if the accident is reportable under the Reporting of Injuries, Diseases and Dangerous Occurrences Regulations (RIDDOR). To report, go to page 4 of this book or go to **http://www.hse.gov.uk/riddor/report.htm**

Please sign the record and date it. Signature _____ Date _____

Accident record

1 About the person who had the accident

Name

Address

Postcode

Occupation

2 About you, the person filling in this record

i *If you did not have the accident write your address and occupation.*

Name

Address

Postcode

Occupation

3 About the accident

i *Continue on the back of this form if you need to.*

When it happened. Date _____ Time _____

Where it happened. State room or place _____

_____

How the accident happened. Give the cause if you can _____

_____

_____

_____

If the person who had the accident suffered an injury, say what it was _____

_____

Please sign the record and date it. Signature _____ Date _____

4 For the employee only

☐ By ticking this box I give my consent to my employer to disclose my personal information and details of the accident which appear on this form to safety representatives and representatives of employee safety for them to carry out the health and safety functions given to them by law.

Signature _____ Date _____

5 For the employer only

Complete this box if the accident is reportable under the Reporting of Injuries, Diseases and Dangerous Occurrences Regulations (RIDDOR). To report, go to page 4 of this book or go to
http://www.hse.gov.uk/riddor/report.htm

Please sign the record and date it. Signature _____ Date _____

Accident record

1   About the person who had the accident

Name _____

Address _____

_____

Postcode

Occupation _____

2   About you, the person filling in this record

i   *If you did not have the accident write your address and occupation.*

Name _____

Address _____

_____

Postcode

Occupation _____

3   About the accident

i   *Continue on the back of this form if you need to.*

When it happened. Date _____ Time _____

Where it happened. State room or place _____

_____

How the accident happened. Give the cause if you can _____

_____

_____

_____

If the person who had the accident suffered an injury, say what it was _____

_____

Please sign the record and date it. Signature _____ Date _____

4   For the employee only

☐ By ticking this box I give my consent to my employer to disclose my personal information and details of the accident which appear on this form to safety representatives and representatives of employee safety for them to carry out the health and safety functions given to them by law.

Signature _____ Date _____

5   For the employer only

Complete this box if the accident is reportable under the Reporting of Injuries, Diseases and Dangerous Occurrences Regulations (RIDDOR). To report, go to page 4 of this book or go to **http://www.hse.gov.uk/riddor/report.htm**

Please sign the record and date it. Signature _____ Date _____

Accident record

Report number:

Report number:

1   About the person who had the accident

Name

Address

Postcode

Occupation

2   About you, the person filling in this record

i   *If you did not have the accident write your address and occupation.*

Name

Address

Postcode

Occupation

3   About the accident

i   *Continue on the back of this form if you need to.*

When it happened. Date _____ Time _____

Where it happened. State room or place _____

How the accident happened. Give the cause if you can _____

If the person who had the accident suffered an injury, say what it was _____

Please sign the record and date it. Signature _____ Date _____

4   For the employee only

☐   By ticking this box I give my consent to my employer to disclose my personal information and details of the accident which appear on this form to safety representatives and representatives of employee safety for them to carry out the health and safety functions given to them by law.

Signature _____ Date _____

5   For the employer only

Complete this box if the accident is reportable under the Reporting of Injuries, Diseases and Dangerous Occurrences Regulations (RIDDOR). To report, go to page 4 of this book or go to **http://www.hse.gov.uk/riddor/report.htm**

Please sign the record and date it. Signature _____ Date _____

Accident record

1   About the person who had the accident

Name

Address

Postcode

Occupation

2   About you, the person filling in this record

i *If you did not have the accident write your address and occupation.*

Name

Address

Postcode

Occupation

3   About the accident

i *Continue on the back of this form if you need to.*

When it happened. Date _____ Time _____

Where it happened. State room or place _____
_____

How the accident happened. Give the cause if you can _____
_____
_____
_____

If the person who had the accident suffered an injury, say what it was _____
_____

Please sign the record and date it. Signature _____ Date _____

4   For the employee only

☐ By ticking this box I give my consent to my employer to disclose my personal information and details of the accident which appear on this form to safety representatives and representatives of employee safety for them to carry out the health and safety functions given to them by law.

Signature _____ Date _____

5   For the employer only

Complete this box if the accident is reportable under the Reporting of Injuries, Diseases and Dangerous Occurrences Regulations (RIDDOR). To report, go to page 4 of this book or go to
http://www.hse.gov.uk/riddor/report.htm

Please sign the record and date it. Signature _____ Date _____

Accident record

1   About the person who had the accident

Name

Address

Postcode

Occupation

2   About you, the person filling in this record

i *If you did not have the accident write your address and occupation.*

Name

Address

Postcode

Occupation

3   About the accident

i *Continue on the back of this form if you need to.*

When it happened. Date _____ Time _____

Where it happened. State room or place _____

How the accident happened. Give the cause if you can _____

If the person who had the accident suffered an injury, say what it was _____

Please sign the record and date it. Signature _____ Date _____

4   For the employee only

☐ By ticking this box I give my consent to my employer to disclose my personal information and details of the accident which appear on this form to safety representatives and representatives of employee safety for them to carry out the health and safety functions given to them by law.

Signature _____ Date _____

5   For the employer only

Complete this box if the accident is reportable under the Reporting of Injuries, Diseases and Dangerous Occurrences Regulations (RIDDOR). To report, go to page 4 of this book or go to **http://www.hse.gov.uk/riddor/report.htm**

Please sign the record and date it. Signature _____ Date _____

Accident record

1 About the person who had the accident

Name

Address

Postcode

Occupation

2 About you, the person filling in this record

i *If you did not have the accident write your address and occupation.*

Name

Address

Postcode

Occupation

3 About the accident

i *Continue on the back of this form if you need to.*

When it happened. Date _____ Time _____

Where it happened. State room or place _____

How the accident happened. Give the cause if you can _____

If the person who had the accident suffered an injury, say what it was _____

Please sign the record and date it. Signature _____ Date _____

4 For the employee only

☐ By ticking this box I give my consent to my employer to disclose my personal information and details of the accident which appear on this form to safety representatives and representatives of employee safety for them to carry out the health and safety functions given to them by law.

Signature _____ Date _____

5 For the employer only

Complete this box if the accident is reportable under the Reporting of Injuries, Diseases and Dangerous Occurrences Regulations (RIDDOR). To report, go to page 4 of this book or go to
http://www.hse.gov.uk/riddor/report.htm

Please sign the record and date it. Signature _____ Date _____

Accident record

1   About the person who had the accident

Name _____

Address _____

Postcode _____

Occupation _____

2   About you, the person filling in this record

i *If you did not have the accident write your address and occupation.*

Name _____

Address _____

Postcode _____

Occupation _____

3   About the accident

i *Continue on the back of this form if you need to.*

When it happened. Date _____ Time _____

Where it happened. State room or place _____

_____

How the accident happened. Give the cause if you can _____

_____

_____

_____

If the person who had the accident suffered an injury, say what it was _____

_____

Please sign the record and date it. Signature _____ Date _____

4   For the employee only

☐ By ticking this box I give my consent to my employer to disclose my personal information and details of the accident which appear on this form to safety representatives and representatives of employee safety for them to carry out the health and safety functions given to them by law.

Signature _____ Date _____

5   For the employer only

Complete this box if the accident is reportable under the Reporting of Injuries, Diseases and Dangerous Occurrences Regulations (RIDDOR). To report, go to page 4 of this book or go to
http://www.hse.gov.uk/riddor/report.htm

Please sign the record and date it. Signature _____ Date _____

Accident record

1 About the person who had the accident

Name

Address

Postcode

Occupation

2 About you, the person filling in this record

i *If you did not have the accident write your address and occupation.*

Name

Address

Postcode

Occupation

3 About the accident

i *Continue on the back of this form if you need to.*

When it happened. Date _____ Time _____

Where it happened. State room or place _____

How the accident happened. Give the cause if you can _____

If the person who had the accident suffered an injury, say what it was _____

Please sign the record and date it. Signature _____ Date _____

4 For the employee only

☐ By ticking this box I give my consent to my employer to disclose my personal information and details of the accident which appear on this form to safety representatives and representatives of employee safety for them to carry out the health and safety functions given to them by law.

Signature _____ Date _____

5 For the employer only

Complete this box if the accident is reportable under the Reporting of Injuries, Diseases and Dangerous Occurrences Regulations (RIDDOR). To report, go to page 4 of this book or go to **http://www.hse.gov.uk/riddor/report.htm**

Please sign the record and date it. Signature _____ Date _____

Report number:

Report number:

Accident record

1   About the person who had the accident

Name _____

Address _____

_____ Postcode _____

Occupation _____

2   About you, the person filling in this record

i   *If you did not have the accident write your address and occupation.*

Name _____

Address _____

_____ Postcode _____

Occupation _____

3   About the accident

i   *Continue on the back of this form if you need to.*

When it happened. Date _____ Time _____

Where it happened. State room or place _____

_____

How the accident happened. Give the cause if you can _____

_____

_____

_____

If the person who had the accident suffered an injury, say what it was _____

_____

Please sign the record and date it. Signature _____ Date _____

4   For the employee only

☐ By ticking this box I give my consent to my employer to disclose my personal information and details of the accident which appear on this form to safety representatives and representatives of employee safety for them to carry out the health and safety functions given to them by law.

Signature _____ Date _____

5   For the employer only

Complete this box if the accident is reportable under the Reporting of Injuries, Diseases and Dangerous Occurrences Regulations (RIDDOR). To report, go to page 4 of this book or go to **http://www.hse.gov.uk/riddor/report.htm**

Please sign the record and date it. Signature _____ Date _____

Accident record

1 About the person who had the accident

Name

Address

Postcode

Occupation

2 About you, the person filling in this record

i *If you did not have the accident write your address and occupation.*

Name

Address

Postcode

Occupation

3 About the accident

i *Continue on the back of this form if you need to.*

When it happened. Date _____ Time _____

Where it happened. State room or place _____

_____

How the accident happened. Give the cause if you can _____

_____

_____

_____

If the person who had the accident suffered an injury, say what it was _____

_____

Please sign the record and date it. Signature _____ Date _____

4 For the employee only

☐ By ticking this box I give my consent to my employer to disclose my personal information and details of the accident which appear on this form to safety representatives and representatives of employee safety for them to carry out the health and safety functions given to them by law.

Signature _____ Date _____

5 For the employer only

Complete this box if the accident is reportable under the Reporting of Injuries, Diseases and Dangerous Occurrences Regulations (RIDDOR). To report, go to page 4 of this book or go to **http://www.hse.gov.uk/riddor/report.htm**

Please sign the record and date it. Signature _____ Date _____

Accident record

1 About the person who had the accident

Name

Address

Postcode

Occupation

2 About you, the person filling in this record

i *If you did not have the accident write your address and occupation.*

Name

Address

Postcode

Occupation

3 About the accident

i *Continue on the back of this form if you need to.*

When it happened. Date _____ Time _____

Where it happened. State room or place _____

_____

How the accident happened. Give the cause if you can _____

_____

_____

_____

If the person who had the accident suffered an injury, say what it was _____

_____

Please sign the record and date it. Signature _____ Date _____

4 For the employee only

☐ By ticking this box I give my consent to my employer to disclose my personal information and details of the accident which appear on this form to safety representatives and representatives of employee safety for them to carry out the health and safety functions given to them by law.

Signature _____ Date _____

5 For the employer only

Complete this box if the accident is reportable under the Reporting of Injuries, Diseases and Dangerous Occurrences Regulations (RIDDOR). To report, go to page 4 of this book or go to **http://www.hse.gov.uk/riddor/report.htm**

Please sign the record and date it. Signature _____ Date _____

Accident record

1   About the person who had the accident

Name

Address

Postcode

Occupation

2   About you, the person filling in this record

i *If you did not have the accident write your address and occupation.*

Name

Address

Postcode

Occupation

3   About the accident

i *Continue on the back of this form if you need to.*

When it happened. Date _____ Time _____

Where it happened. State room or place _____

_____

How the accident happened. Give the cause if you can _____

_____

_____

_____

If the person who had the accident suffered an injury, say what it was _____

_____

Please sign the record and date it. Signature _____ Date _____

4   For the employee only

☐ By ticking this box I give my consent to my employer to disclose my personal information and details of the accident which appear on this form to safety representatives and representatives of employee safety for them to carry out the health and safety functions given to them by law.

Signature _____ Date _____

5   For the employer only

Complete this box if the accident is reportable under the Reporting of Injuries, Diseases and Dangerous Occurrences Regulations (RIDDOR). To report, go to page 4 of this book or go to **http://www.hse.gov.uk/riddor/report.htm**

Please sign the record and date it. Signature _____ Date _____

Accident record

1 About the person who had the accident

Name

Address

Postcode

Occupation

2 About you, the person filling in this record

i *If you did not have the accident write your address and occupation.*

Name

Address

Postcode

Occupation

3 About the accident

i *Continue on the back of this form if you need to.*

When it happened. Date _____ Time _____

Where it happened. State room or place _____

_____

How the accident happened. Give the cause if you can _____

_____

_____

_____

If the person who had the accident suffered an injury, say what it was _____

_____

Please sign the record and date it. Signature _____ Date _____

---

4 For the employee only

☐ By ticking this box I give my consent to my employer to disclose my personal information and details of the accident which appear on this form to safety representatives and representatives of employee safety for them to carry out the health and safety functions given to them by law.

Signature _____ Date _____

---

5 For the employer only

Complete this box if the accident is reportable under the Reporting of Injuries, Diseases and Dangerous Occurrences Regulations (RIDDOR). To report, go to page 4 of this book or go to **http://www.hse.gov.uk/riddor/report.htm**

Please sign the record and date it. Signature _____ Date _____

Report number:

Report number: